A narrow beam of sunlight penetrates
deep into Upper Antelope Canyon

▲ The Bear in Upper Antelope Canyon

THIS IS
Slot Canyons

▲ The cathedral of the first chamber of Upper Antelope Canyon

Copyright © 2014 by:
Park Partners, Inc.
Henderson, NV

Website: nationalparksusa.com
Email: parkpartnersinc@gmail.com
ISBN: 978-1-58071-131-9
Printed in the Republic of South Korea
Author: Christopher K. Eaton
Photography: Christopher K. Eaton, Charly Moore
Publisher: Kevin Poulson
Book Design: Karen A. D'Amore, Fizzy Feather Designs

▶ Reflected sunlight reaching deep into Canyon X

Shafts of late-morning sunlight, Lower Antelope Canyon

▲ Looking up through Lower Antelope Canyon

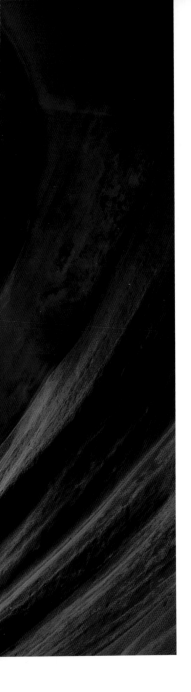

THIS IS

SLOT CANYON

The slot canyons of the Navajo Sandstone formation on the Colorado Plateau are an example of nature's artistic aspirations. Carved by the flow of moving water, these canyons corkscrew and swirl and plunge right through the heart of the ancient petrified sand dunes exposed by the uplift of the Colorado Plateau over the last several million years. As the force of flash floods take advantage of cracks and fissures in the surface, the flow of water over stone has slowly carved and polished its way deeper and deeper into the landscape. The sides of these canyons feature curves and lines and shadows like no other. At times smooth and sinuous, at times scalloped and sharp-cornered, the path of these slot canyons rarely take a straight line—both horizontally and vertically.

As if to highlight the artistic nature of these slot canyons, the upper and lower slots of Antelope Canyon have been given very inspirational names by the local Native Americans of the region. Upper Antelope Canyon is known to the Navajo as *Tse' bighanilini*, which means "the place where water runs through rocks". Lower Antelope Canyon's Navajo name is *Hasdestwazi*, or "spiral rock arches".

▲ Sandfall, third chamber of Upper Antelope Canyon

▲ A shaft of sunlight through The Corkscrew of Upper Antelope Canyon

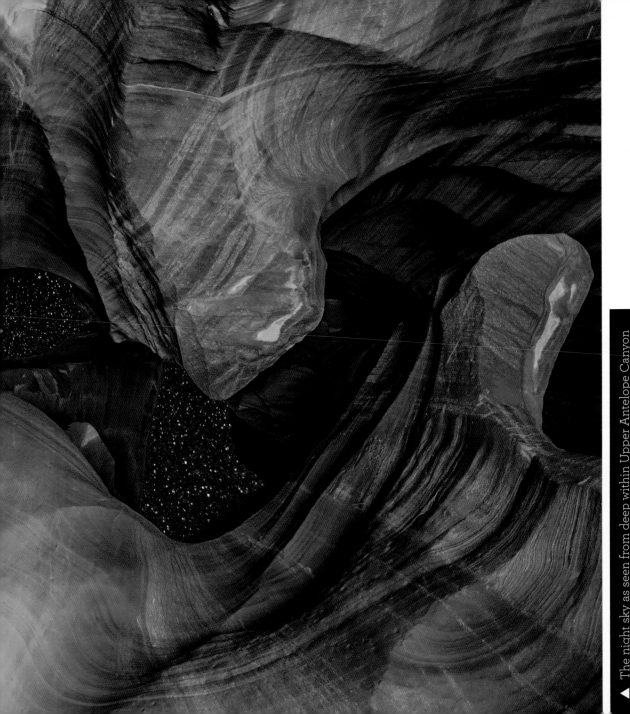

▲ The night sky as seen from deep within Upper Antelope Canyon

During the Jurassic Period, 180-190 million years ago, most of Utah and Arizona, as well as parts of Idaho, Wyoming, Colorado, New Mexico, Nevada, and California, were covered by the Navajo Erg—an eolian, or wind deposited, sand dune desert covering approximately 850,000 square miles at its largest extent. This is larger than the combined size of the various sand dune fields of the modern Sahara Desert of Northern Africa. Today, this erg is preserved in the petrified sand dunes of Navajo, Aztec, and Nugget Sandstones, depending on where they are found on and around the Colorado Plateau. For example, the red cliffs of Red Rock National Conservation Area

west of Las Vegas, Nevada, are the Aztec Sandstone Formation. Navajo Sandstone is one of the geologic highlights at the heart of the Colorado Plateau; it is found in Glen Canyon National Recreation Area, Grand Staircase-Escalante National Monument, Rainbow Bridge National Monument, Zion National Park, Capitol Reef National Park, Dinosaur National Monument, Flaming Gorge National Recreation Area, Canyonlands National Park, Arches National Park, Coral Pink Sand Dunes State Park, and Snow Canyon State Park.

▲ The Grotto in Red Canyon

Lower Antelope Canyon is a narrow, twisting passage through the Navajo Sandstone

As ancient mountain ranges to the east—the Ancestral Rocky Mountains and possibly the Appalachian Mountains—eroded, large swaths of quartz sand were deposited by rivers flowing toward the modern day Colorado Plateau. These sandy sediments were picked up by the prevailing winds that blew them into the open flood plains where they were deposited. As more and more sand was blown into the region, it migrated with the winds, merging and expanding sand dune ergs. Sand dunes built upon sand dunes over millions of years until the Navajo Erg covered most of what is now the American Southwest. In addition to covering a vast area, this erg reached impressive depths. At its thickest in Zion National Park, the Navajo Sandstone is approximately 2,500 feet (762 meters) thick with nearly 2,300 feet (700 meters) of it exposed in its cliffs. The exposure of sandstone in other areas varies from 1,000 feet in Glen Canyon National Recreation Area to hundreds of feet at the top of Canyonlands National Park to surface exposure as the bedrock that Arches National Park rises from.

▶ As late-morning sunlight pours into Lower Antelope Canyon, the reflection from one wall sets the opposite wall on fire

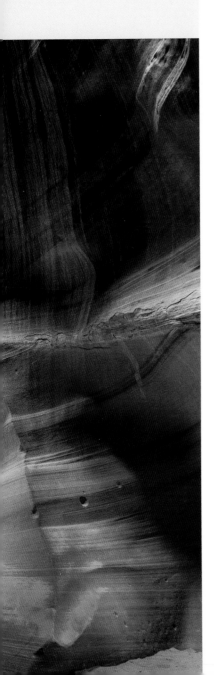

On a more local scale, the Navajo Sandstone is built with layer upon layer of cross-bedded sandstone. As the prevailing winds carried sand from the erosion of mountains and the existing sand dunes migrated with these winds, the sand was deposited in thin, angled layers; the orientation of the angle indicates wind direction. As these winds shifted in direction, so did the orientation of deposition. It is common to see sets of tilted layers built upon each other, each angled in different directions. It is this feature of the sandstone that is one of the primary factors in the artistic formation of these slot canyons.

As moving water flows through the canyon, it slowly carves and polishes the sandstone, exposing these cross-bedded layers. Like crashing waves of sand, they converge and diverge from all angles; they start as thin, compressed lines that flare out as they progress along the wall; they erode as undulating layers where the shadows of each define the whole.

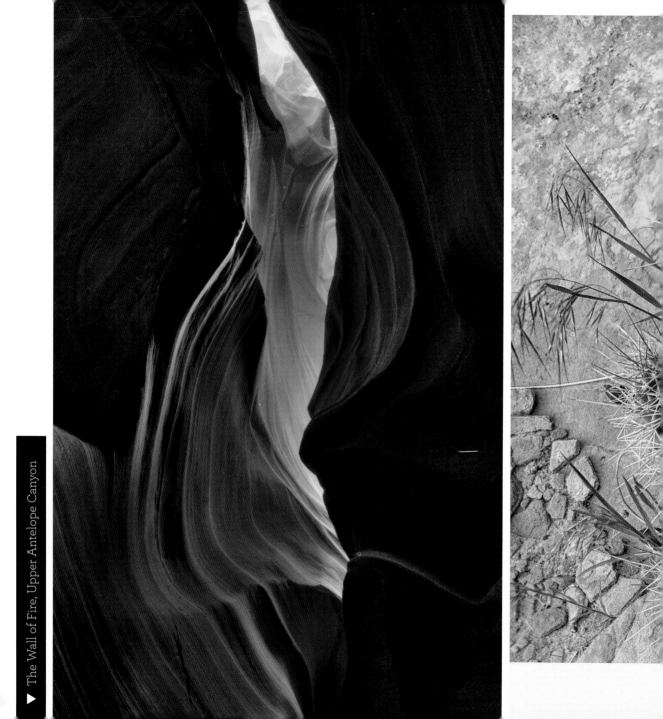

▶ The Wall of Fire, Upper Antelope Canyon

▲ Claret Cup cactus (*Echinocereus triglochidiatus*) grows in rocky areas of the canyons and boldly blooms in the spring

▲ Impassible crack through a wall of Canyon X is only six inches wide

▲ Wind and water leave behind detritus in Canyon X

How does a massive sand dune erg become a thick layer of sandstone covering a large area of landscape? The region that would become the Colorado Plateau rested at sea level for most of the past few hundred million years. Below the Navajo Sandstone rests more than 300 million years of deposited mudstones, sandstones, limestones, etc. from inland seas, large lakes, tidal flats, and river systems. And for the 120-130 million years after the building of this massive region of sand dunes, the area continued to accumulate more sediments. It is estimated that 14,000-18,000 feet of sedimentary layers were deposited in the region before uplift began. The record of this long period of deposition is not complete however; erosion removed thousands of feet of rock layers both before and after the Navajo Sandstone. It is possible that the region was buried under even more eolian sand than the 2,500 feet of sandstone currently exposed on the Colorado Plateau.

▶ Dancing flame of light, Upper Antelope Canyon

▲ A Prairie Rattlesnake (*Crotalus viridis*) emerges in spring, Canyon X

▲ Plateau Fence Lizard (*Sceloporus tristichus*) hunting insects, Canyon X

Common Side-Blotched Lizard
(*Uta stansburiana*), Canyon X

▲ Great Basin Gophersnake (*Pituophis catenifer deserticola*) hiding in the rocks of Canyon X

▶ Mud cracks after a flash flood through Canyon X

▲ Upper Antelope Canyon under the stars

▲ Bright, reflected light fades to rich shadows deep in Upper Antelope Canyon

Everything changed around 70 million years ago when the landscape began to rise. Regional uplift caused bulging and fracturing of the rock layers beginning the creation of the Colorado Plateau as well as the modern Rocky Mountains. Erosion became the predominate force working on the landscape; a force that dominates to this day. The region continued to rise for millions of years creating a number of bulges in the rock layers where these ancient sediments were twisted and bent and exposed. River systems flowing east carved through these layers as uplift continued to force millions of years of rock upward. The landscape we see today began to take shape between 10 and 5 million years ago when the Grand Canyon took its final shape. Exactly how this happened is still being debated by geologists, but during this time it is likely that rivers flowing east changed direction, possibly integrating with rivers flowing west, creating the modern Colorado River, and her tributaries, and the modern landscape was born.

▲ Ghostly light beam, Upper Antelope Canyon

▲ Soft beam of sunlight drops through the heart of Upper Antelope Canyon

▲ A brief beam of sunlight, Canyon X

▲ Solstice light reaching into Canyon X

▶ Mid-morning sunlight passes through the Antelope's Eye

▼ An arch in Peek-a-Boo Canyon in the Escalante River drainage

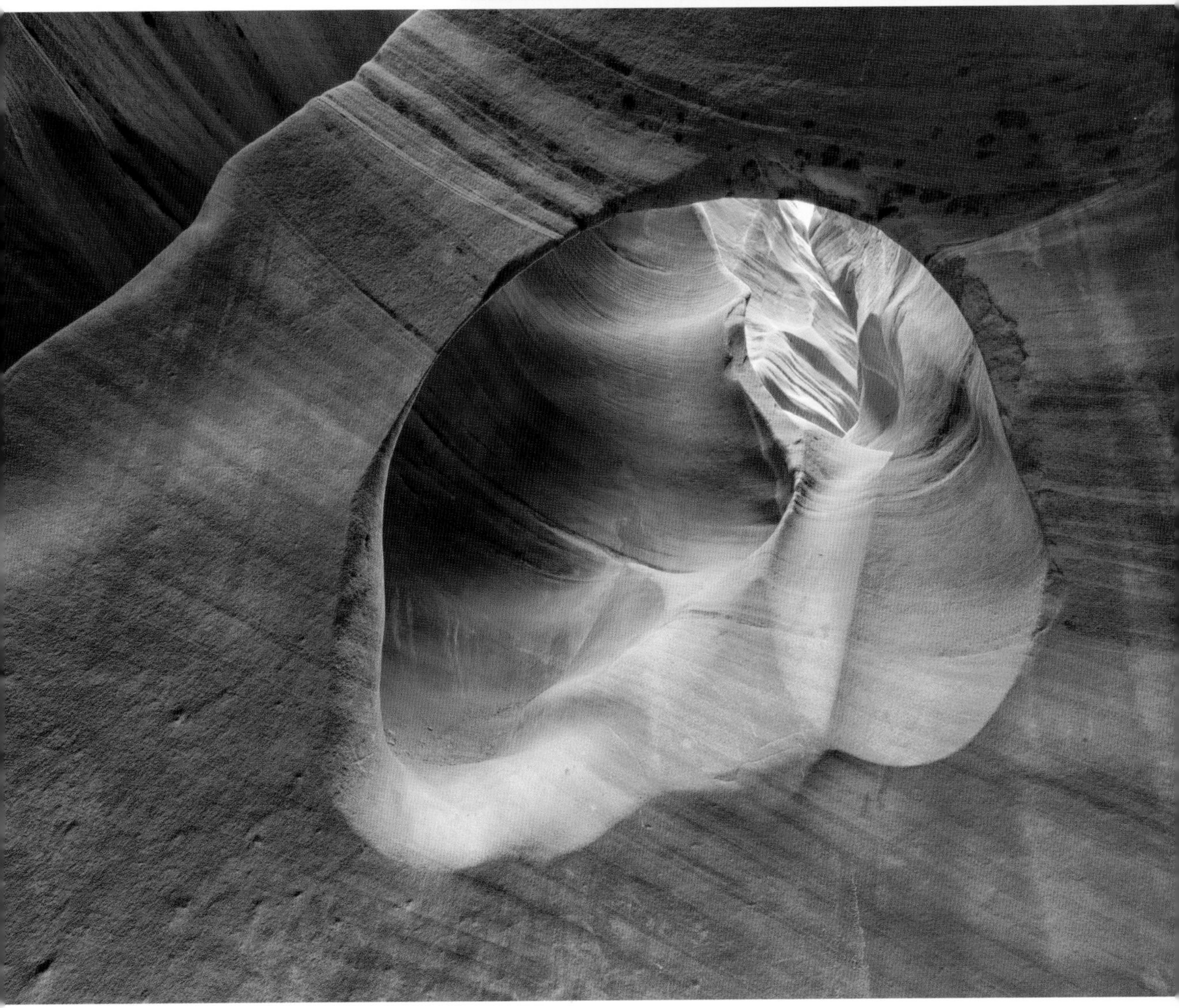

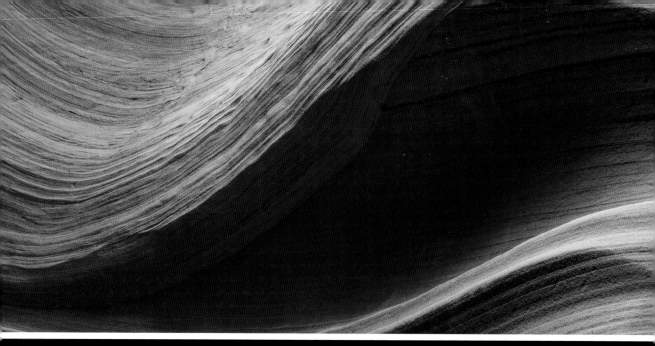

▲ Swirls of cross-bedded Navajo Sandstone, Canyon X   ▶ A flash floods pours through Canyon X

When did the slot canyons of the Navajo Sandstone form? The modern Colorado Plateau landscape has been around for close to 2 million years. The dominant erosional force on this landscape is the Colorado River and its tributaries, which have been carving through the exposed layers for millions of years. Most of the slot canyons, such as Antelope Canyon (the most famous slot canyon on the Colorado Plateau if not the world), have likely been carved over the last few hundreds of thousands of years as flowing water works its way into cracks and fissures in the sandstone. These canyons often form in the smaller streams of the Colorado River and its major tributaries such as the Escalante, Dirty Devil, San Juan, and Paria Rivers. These waterways are often dry much of the year, but are subject to the brief, but large flow of water and debris of a flash flood.

▲ Shadowed light deep in Upper Antelope Canyon brings out the blues

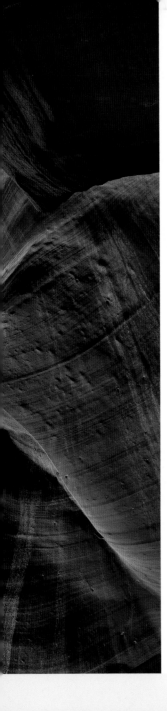

The erosional process is slow and rarely seen from year-to-year. During the monsoon season, when large amounts of rain can fall from passing thunderstorms in a short period of time, an inch of rain or more over a local area of sand and slickrock moves across the landscape collecting into large, fast moving flash floods. These flood waters often contain sand, silt, gravels, and logs, all of which can be abrasive forces working on the walls and floors of the slot canyons. While suspended sand and small rocks in the flood waters work slowly to carve and polish, to shape and form the walls of the canyons, it is the gravel and other large debris moving along the bottom of the flow that carves into the floor of the canyon. This explains why the slot canyons are usually narrow and deep—the downward carving action is the predominate abrasion of the canyon. Other forces create the sinuous nature of the canyons. As water forces its way through the narrow passages of the canyons, turbulence and cavitation create the curved and scalloped edges that any artist would admire.

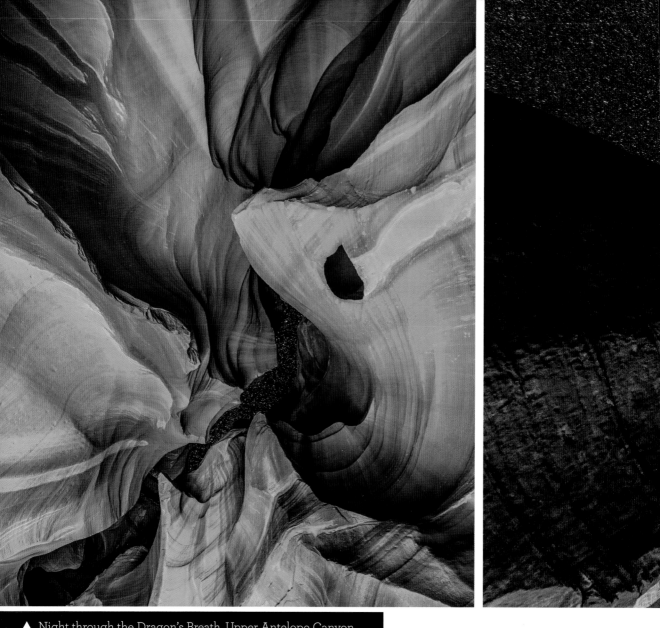

▲ Night through the Dragon's Breath, Upper Antelope Canyon

▲ The Milky Way rises above Upper Antelope Canyon

Slot canyons come in various shapes and sizes. Canyons like Antelope Canyon and parts of Canyon X may only be a few feet wide at the top, but are cavernous at their bottom a hundred feet or more below. While both sections of Antelope Canyon are also long as well as deep, the slots of Canyon X are little shorter, but no less impressive. The upper slot of Antelope Canyon is essentially flat with a sandy floor throughout, while the lower slot features a series of pourovers, or dry falls, that require ladders to navigate and its floor is often narrow and sharply curved. Some canyons are even so narrow that passage would be impossible by humans.

Throughout the Colorado Plateau region, many slot canyons cut through remote locations that require miles of overland travel to locate; and, once there, they often require technical climbing and canyoneering skills and the gear that accompanies such an expedition. The very nature of how these canyons are carved often dictates the creation of an inaccessible landscape only traversed by ravens and owls and other small birds that nest high in the canyons along with the lizards and small rodents they dine upon.

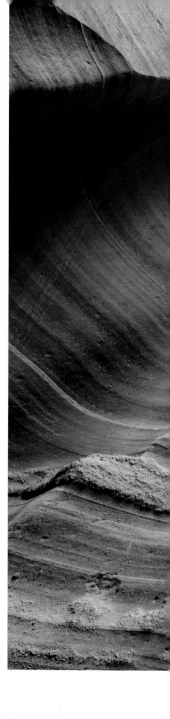

▲ Lower Antelope Canyon carves deeply into the sandstone requiring ladders to descend into areas where moving water plunges downward

▶ Early-morning light in the back of Secret Canyon

▲ Passage through Mountain Sheep Canyon

▲ Swirling curves of cross-bedded Navajo Sandstone in Canyon X

Navajo Sandstone is one of the geologic strata of the Colorado Plateau that gives this landscape one of its unofficial names... Red Rock Country. Most exposures of the sandstone are colored various hues of red. Each quartz sand crystal is coated with a thin film of hematite, one of the oxidized forms of iron. Where the sandstone is more of a white color, the iron was "bleached" from the sandstone by hydrocarbon-laced water that passed through the sandstone while buried deep below the surface; these hydrocarbons deoxidized the hematite allowing the iron to be transported elsewhere.

Another artistic aspect of the slot canyons of the Navajo Sandstone is the various colors and hues that can be seen from deep within the canyons. Though the sandstone is red in color, it often also displays shades of yellow, orange, pink, purple, and occasionally blue. Because of the narrow upper reaches of the canyons, sunlight usually only strikes the sandstone directly near the top; from there, it reflects back and forth off the canyon walls as it slowly filters downward. The bouncing light will change color the deeper it reaches, from yellow to orange to pink to purple. Shades of blue deep within the canyon are the result of this light reflecting off minerals deposited on the stone by slow moving water coating the rock with a desert varnish.

▲ Rocks on fire in Lower Antelope Canyon

▲ A hanging window arch, Lower Antelope Canyon

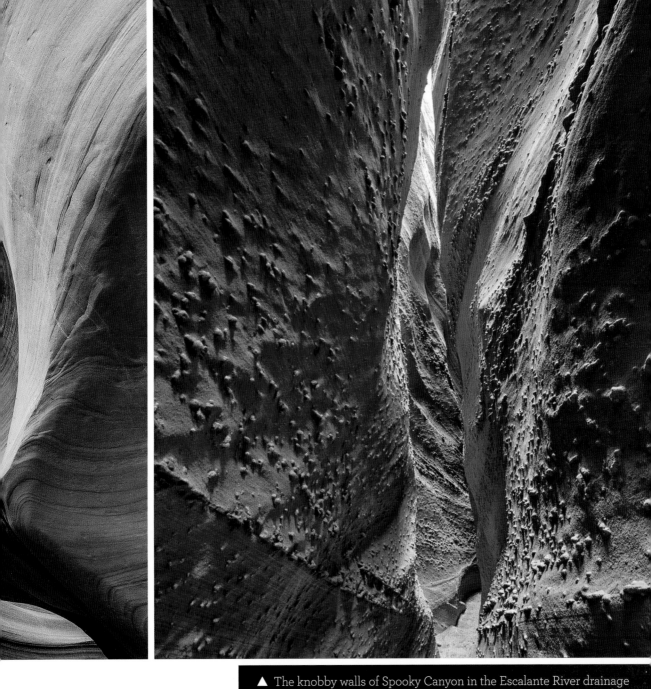

▲ The knobby walls of Spooky Canyon in the Escalante River drainage

▼ Lava-red light descending in Canyon X

Slot canyons are not to be trifled with. Beyond the difficulties in travel that some canyons present, and the dangers that their remoteness may pose due to the very nature of the desert environment, ALL slot canyons are dangerous. Flash floods present the greatest danger and even a small flood 12-inches deep in open land has enough force to sweep humans off their feet and carry them downstream. In a slot canyon, flash floods are a recipe for disaster. Acting under the same principle as water forced through a pipe or hose under pressure, a slot canyon amplifies the flow of a flash flood, accelerating the water and debris to extreme velocities, and the narrow, sinuous nature of slot canyons create turbulence and eddies that can trap anything in the water in an endless spiral along the abrasive canyon walls. Logs and debris wedged 40 feet or more above the canyon floor attest to the depth and power of these floods.

Do not enter any slot canyon if storms are present or are within 30-50 miles upstream. Flash floods can travel from miles away carrying the rain of a distant storm to a place with blue skies. The National Weather Service often issues flash flood warnings when the threat is high, but do not rely on the absence of such a warning as an indicator of safety. Summer thunderstorms can form quickly and dump an inch or more of rain on a landscape in less than an hour.

▲ Young coyote pup (*Canis latrans*) rests in Canyon X

▲ The narrow way through Zebra Canyon

The artistic beauty of the slot canyons of the Navajo Sandstone is incomparable. Found in a landscape of unmatched beauty in its own right, these works of natural sculpture are each unique. Photographs can only partially capture their true nature. They reveal their colors, depth, and form; and they can reveal the nature of the artist's relationship with the canyon. But, photographs can only go so far. To truly understand a slot canyon, it needs to be experienced in person, its essence distilled from the dusty air and reflected light, from its deep caverns and narrow, curvy passages. *When visiting a slot canyon, please respect it as a force of nature and as a place unique and rare; travel softly and leave no trace.*

▲ A finger of rock protrudes into the curves of Secret Canyon

▲ The sun bursts through a narrow opening in Canyon X

▲ Night through the Dragon's Teeth, Upper Antelope Canyon

▲ Deep within Canyon X

▲ Deep within Upper Antelope Cany

▲ The full Moon rises above the entrance to Upper Antelope Canyon

Photo Credits

All photos are copyright of the photographers
In order of appearance:

Front Cover
A narrow beam of sunlight penetrates deep into Upper Antelope Canyon
Christopher K. Eaton

The Bear in Upper Antelope Canyon
Christopher K. Eaton

Title Page
The cathedral of the first chamber in Upper Antelope Canyon
Charly Moore

Reflected sunlight reaching deep into Canyon X
Christopher K. Eaton

Shafts of late-morning sunlight, Lower Antelope Canyon
Charly Moore

Crashing waves of stone, Canyon X
Christopher K. Eaton

Looking up through Lower Antelope Canyon
Christopher K. Eaton

Sandfall, third chamber of Upper Antelope Canyon
Charly Moore

A shaft of sunlight through the Corkscrew of Upper Antelope Canyon
Christopher K. Eaton

The night sky as seen from deep within Upper Antelope Canyon
Christopher K. Eaton

Lady in the Wind Arch, Lower Antelope Canyon
Christopher K. Eaton

The Grotto in Red Canyon
Christopher K. Eaton

Lower Antelope Canyon is a narrow, twisting passage through the Navajo Sandstone
Christopher K. Eaton

The Guardian of Lower Antelope Canyon
Charly Moore

As late-morning sunlight pours into Lower Antelope Canyon, the reflection from one wall sets the opposite wall on fire
Christopher K. Eaton

Falling sand is illuminated by a shaft of sunlight in Upper Antelope Canyon
Christopher K. Eaton

The Wall of Fire, Upper Antelope Canyon
Charly Moore

Claret Cup cactus (*Echinocereus triglochidiatus*) grows in rocky areas of the canyons and boldly blooms in the spring
Charly Moore

Impassible crack through a wall of Canyon X is only six inches wide
Christopher K. Eaton

Wind and water leave behind detritus in Canyon X
Christopher K. Eaton

Dancing flame of light, Upper Antelope Canyon
Christopher K. Eaton

A Prairie Rattlesnake (*Crotalus viridis*) emerges in spring, Canyon X
Charly Moore

Plateau Fence Lizard (*Sceloporus tristichus*) hunting insects, Canyon X
Christopher K. Eaton

Common Side-Blotched Lizard (*Uta stansburiana*), Canyon X
Christopher K. Eaton

Great Basin Gophersnake (*Pituophis catenifer deserticola*) hiding in the rocks of Canyon X
Charly Moore

Mud cracks after a flash flood through Canyon X
Christopher K. Eaton

Upper Antelope Canyon under the stars
Charly Moore

Bright, reflected light fades to rich shadows deep in Upper Antelope Canyon
Charly Moore

Ghostly light beam, Upper Antelope Canyon
Christopher K. Eaton

Soft beam of sunlight drops through the heart of Upper Antelope Canyon
Charly Moore

A brief beam of sunlight, Canyon X
Christopher K. Eaton

Solstice light reaching into Canyon X
Charly Moore

Mid-morning sunlight passes through the Antelope's Eye
Christopher K. Eaton

An arch in Peek-a-Boo Canyon in the Escalante River drainage
Charly Moore

Swirls of cross-bedded Navajo Sandstone, Canyon X
Christopher K. Eaton

A flash floods pours through Canyon X
Charly Moore

Shadowed light deep in Upper Antelope Canyon brings out the blues
Christopher K. Eaton

Night through the Dragon's Breath, Upper Antelope Canyon
Christopher K. Eaton

The Milky Way rises above Upper Antelope Canyon
Christopher K. Eaton

Lower Antelope Canyon carves deeply into the sandstone requiring ladders to descend into areas where moving water plunges downward
Christopher K. Eaton

Early-morning light in the back of Secret Canyon
Christopher K. Eaton

Passage through Mountain Sheep Canyon
Charly Moore

Starry, starry night through Upper Antelope Canyon
Christopher K. Eaton

Swirling curves of cross-bedded Navajo Sandstone in Canyon X
Christopher K. Eaton

Rocks on fire in Lower Antelope Canyon
Christopher K. Eaton

A hanging window arch, Lower Antelope Canyon
Christopher K. Eaton

The knobby walls of Spooky Canyon in the Escalante River drainage
Charly Moore

Lava-red light descending in Canyon X
Christopher K. Eaton

Young coyote pup (*Canis latrans*) rests in Canyon X
Charly Moore

The narrow way through Zebra Canyon
Charly Moore

A finger of rock protrudes into the curves of Secret Canyon
Charly Moore

The sun bursts through a narrow opening in Canyon X
Charly Moore

Night through the Dragon's Teeth, Upper Antelope Canyon
Christopher K. Eaton

Deep within Canyon X
Christopher K. Eaton

Deep within Upper Antelope Canyon
Christopher K. Eaton

The full Moon rises above the entrace to Upper Antelope Canyon
Charly Moore

Back Cover
Fall morning light glows in the back of Secret Canyon
Christopher K. Eaton

▶ Fall morning light glows in the back of Secret Ca

9/23